Santa's Early Christmas
Lily Lawson

Published by

THE
WRIGHT HOUSE

Santa started Christmas early.
Well, he had a good excuse,

He ate up all the sweet mince pies
and drank up all the juice.

The cheeseboard was quite empty
by the time he got to lunch.

So, he had to just have crackers
as he drank up all the punch.

He couldn't resist finishing
Mrs. Claus' trifle
As he licked the spoon clean
a yawn he had to stifle.

Santa's feeling happy now
the presents are on time.
Everything is as it should be
he knew it would be fine.

You better watch out

You better watch out, I'm telling you why,
Rudolph the reindeer is learning to fly.
He jumps off the rooftops and into the sky,
and lands in a heap, he doesn't know why.

The other reindeer they all zoom around,
he can't join in as he can't leave the ground.
The laughing and teasing is all out of hand,
They just can't get it, they don't understand.

Santa says that if Rudolph can believe
He'll be pulling his sleigh on Christmas Eve.
'If you keep on trying - you'll get there, you'll see!
Practice as much as you can, that's the key'

Rudolph trains in secret every day
He's nearly ready to pull Santa's sleigh
But just to be safe, you had better watch out
You just can't be sure when Rudolph's about!

Christmas Tingles

Lights and toys and tinsel
are hung upon the tree
The colours of a Christmas
are there for all to see.

The cards have all been written.
The presents wrapped with care.
Waiting for the day itself,
and we are nearly there.

Here's hoping that your Christmas
is a happy one for you
and that very special feeling
will last the whole year through.

Now you've read my book
don't forget to review
Amazon, Goodreads,
Bookbub too!
Thank you very much
I'm counting on you!

Lily x

Acknowledgements

Thank so much to my illustrator Gustyawan
and my elves -

Cheryl, David, Dreena, Kimberly, Jo, Julie,
Kim, Anita, Ann

Helen, Laura, Lamia, Imelda, Morgan, Stacey, Ash
and their mini elves

Cin and Tracey
Christine
my dad

and to all of you for reading my book.

By the author

My Father's Daughter

'My Father's Daughter, a collection of poems
ranging from light-hearted to heart-rending,
captures Lily Lawson's thoughtful observations
about life and love.'

A Taste of What's to Come

A selection of accessible, relatable, eclectic poetry.
Each piece tells its story in only the way Lily can.

Rainbow's Red Book of Poetry

Weaving through love and hate,
I rise from the ashes, my words you own –
I am red.

A poem from Rainbow's Red Book of Poetry

Parenting

Love was looking for their children.

Kindness was helping people.
Compassion was listening.
Understanding was mediating.
Faith was encouraging.
Hope was sharing joy.

Love stopped looking for their children;
they were out in the world making a difference,
as Love taught them.

About the author

Lily Lawson is a poet and fiction writer living in the UK.

She has poetry, short stories and creative non-fiction published in anthologies and online

in addition to her poetry books

My Fathers Daughter, A Taste of What's to Come, and Rainbow's Red Book of Poetry.

You can find out more about Lily and read more of her work on her blog.

Subscribers to Life with Lily are the first to hear all her writing news. You can sign up here.

Printed in Great Britain
by Amazon

25534760R00027